Food Galleria

The daughter of the original Spider-Man, May "Mayday" Parker, has inherited her father's amazing powers. Possessing the proportionate strength, speed and agility of a spider, as well as the ability to cling to walls, she now follows in his web-lines!

Stan Lee presents

SPIDER-GIRL!

UNFINISHED BUSINESS!

50%

Tom DeFalco &
Pat Olliffe
script, plot & pencils
Al Williamson
inker
Dave Sharpe
letterer
Christie Scheele
colorist
Frank Dunkerly asst. editor
Matt Hicks editor
Joe Quesada editor in chief

Your name is May "**Mayday**" Parker, and you are the daughter of the one, true *Spider-Man*.

Unfortunately, you recently lost the amazing spider-like powers you inherited from your father.

(Bummer!)

That means you can no longer be *Spider-Girl.*

(Major bummer!)

Also means you can now sleep in on school mornings--

--instead of getting up at *5:00 A.M.* to practice your powers with daddy dearest!

(The proverbial silver lining!)

Ironic, isn't it? He didn't even want you to do the spider-thing at first, but your mother was supportive.

Now he's all fretful, and Mom just seems relieved.

'Morning! Call off the search parties-- she's awake at last!

Can I make you some eggs, hon?

Not only did it help me avoid many a minor mishap, but I also loved using it to nail super-foes.

Wh-what do you mean?

You know how the spider-sense instinctively warns us of danger?

It also indicates where an adversary's the *least* dangerous--

--so that you can direct all your efforts on his weak point.

Catch you later, Dad.

I'm off.

Uhhhh...

Yeah.

Sure.

I have basketball practice today, Mom-- so I won't be home until dinnertime.

Have a good day, hotshot!

⸮Ahem⸮

Is it my imagination, or did she just point out an ability you never even knew you had?

We have any more toast?

Hey, Moose! *Moose!*

Where have you been, guy?

If I didn't know better, I'd think you've been avoiding me.

D-don't be mental, Courtney! I've just been, *you know,* kind o' busy.

You want to meet in the cafeteria for lunch--

--or go for a soda after school?

Maybe some other time.

I... uhhhh... already got plans.

S-sure.

No problem.

Some other time.

Why the long face, Yama? You look like you just lost your best bud.

I have...

...sorta.

Courtney Duran and I used to spend all our spare time together.

We're just friends, *you know,* but it was nice hanging with her.

Then she started dating Moose, and... welllll...she doesn't have as much time for me.

Now she and Moose are on the outs, and I *should* be glad...

...but I keep thinking she's *happier* with him--

--and I should try to get them back together.

Are you completely whacked out? Moose dropped her because he thinks she's cheating on him with JJ.

Trust me, man-- this is one love triangle you definitely want to avoid.

Let them sort it out for them-selves!

You'll only get in trouble if you interfere.

Raptor is going down!

I am so glad you called, May.

I just heard about Raptor's recent escapades.

She will never escape *Phil Urich, the GOLDEN GOBLIN!*

Since you've lost your spider-powers, I'd be honored to go after her for you.

Actually, Uncle Phil...

...that's not *quite* what I have in *mind.*

Moose! We need to talk. Seriously talk.

Oh, yeah? *Tough!* I've got no interest in anything you have to say. 'Specially if it's about Court. I've decided to move on.

I...I don't believe it.

You're a *coward.*

WHAT--?!

To think I used to be afraid of you. The big bully is a total, total wuss.

You gone WHACK-O, Yama-- --or just tired o' having TEETH?!

You want to pound on me?

Go for it!

It won't change the fact that you're wimping out on Courtney.

Stuff it, Yama! The girl made a choice, and I'm man enough to respect her decision.

Sounds awfully *noble!* Too bad you're just a dumb jock who leaped to the *wrong* conclusion.

She and JJ bonded when they were both kidnapped by those *Savage Six* guys a few weeks ago.*

They're just *friends,* idiot!

Just FRIENDS!

*See Spider-Girl #25

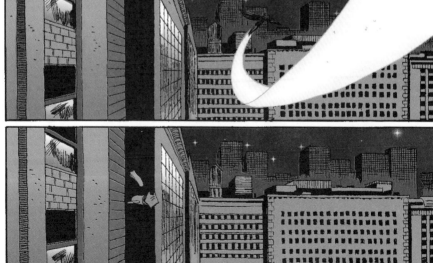

KWAM BOOM!

RWDOOM!

Raptor, *old buddy, old pal*, I hate to intrude on your solitude, but--*hey!* This night is too beautiful to waste.

I'm thinking we girls need to kick into party mode, and experience a total *fighto-mania!*

SPIDER-GIRL?!

W-where'd you come from?

And what are you *doing* on that ridiculous-looking... *whatever the heck it is!*

I'm haunted by some of the stupid and vicious things I've done--

--and I'm just trying to make amends.

Listen, Spider-Girl-- *I don't want to fight anymore.* How's about we give the punches a pass?

Sure, but only if you *surrender!*

If you think a few bags of groceries make up for putting that courier in a wheelchair--

--you really need to catch a clue!

Please don't misunderstand me, girlfriend! While I may be going through a major case of the *guilts*--

--I'm far from being down with any *jail time!*

This is one girl who needs to spread her wings!

You can't compensate for past deeds by *stealing,* Rap.

You need to get off the crime treadmill.

A good lawyer might be able to get you off with a-- *heyyyy!*

Where'd you go?

VOTE
TON

Hey, Courtney! *Courtney!*

M-Moose?

Wh-what are you doing here?

I was hoping to catch you on your way home from the school library.

Look, Court... I...I know that I've been behaving like a real bonehead lately.

I...I'm *sorry.*

I-it's just that I really, *realllllly* like you--

--and I was scared that you didn't like me anymore.

Oh, Moosie!

You really *are* a bonehead--

--but you're *my* bonehead!

BZZZZZZ

Your name is May "Mayday" Parker--

--and you are no longer the *web-swinger* you once were.

Suck it up, girl! It's crunch time, and you're determined to build up your strength and endurance--

--and to learn whatever skills are necessary to become a *different* kind of web-swinger.

You're going to claw your way back into the hero biz--

--even if it *kills* you!

THE END...
for now!

≑Whew≑ That girl plays rough.

Maybe it's because she trained her whole life to be a crime-fighter--

--and doesn't have any patience for someone without the necessary skills to survive on the streets.

What are you trying to *prove*, May?

I can't quit being *Spider-Girl* until I bring *Raptor* to justice.

You *must* understand--

--or you wouldn't have lent me your *Golden Goblin* gear to go after her the other night.

You should have hung up your costume on the day you lost your powers.

I...I know, Uncle Phil... but I still have some loose ends to tie up.

A fat lot of good that did! You crashed my Goblin glider, and nearly killed yourself!

It's time to for a reality check, May-- *you can't play Spider-Girl without your powers!*

B-but you used to be so supportive.

And *you* used to have the proportionate strength, speed and agility of a spider!

Please, Uncle Phil...

...I need your help more than ever.

Forget it, May! As far as I'm concerned--

--you've spun your last WEB!

You want to WHAT?!

Why the volume, Mom? I don't need super powers to be a hero.

There are plenty of costumed athletes like *American Dream* and the *Ladyhawks*.

Where is all this *dedication* suddenly coming from?

Aren't you the girl who couldn't be bothered to chase fleeing muggers?

Am I missing something? You used to encourage responsibility.

Don't even try to play me like that!

Without your powers, you may be an above-average athlete--

--but you're still no match for guys with guns.

Yeah.

Sure.

What-ever!

Where are you going now?

Out!

To visit a friend--

--of the non-spandex variety!

Non-spandex variety--?!

What can I say, Normie? She brings out the drama queen in me.

Look, May, I have to be honest...

...she *does* have a point.

Duhhhh!

I know she's right... and I actually agree with her. But I still have this *Raptor*-thing hanging over me.

Don't get me wrong, kid-- I hope you *never* quit!

For *Raptor's* sake, as well as yours!

If it weren't for you, I'd still be the *Green Goblin!*

The world needs heroes like *Spider-Girl!*

And my grandfather is probably turning over in his grave to hear any *Osborn* say that to a *Parker.*

I appreciate the support, Normie--*more than you can ever imagine*--but I don't have a choice.

Want to bet?

I may have a solution to your problem.

You up for a field trip?

Are you really allowed to leave the sanitarium?

Yeah, but I may have to tell a *white lie*--

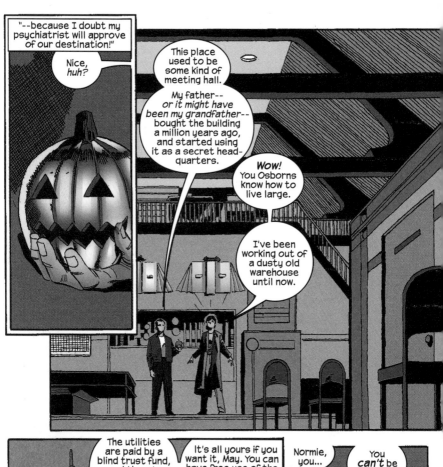

"--because I doubt my psychiatrist will approve of our destination!"

Nice, huh?

This place used to be some kind of meeting hall.

My father-- or it might have been my grandfather-- bought the building a million years ago, and started using it as a secret head-quarters.

Wow! You Osborns know how to live large.

I've been working out of a dusty old warehouse until now.

The utilities are paid by a blind trust fund, and there's even a hidden entrance in the bell tower.

It's all yours if you want it, May. You can have free use of the building and any of my old Goblin gimmicks or weapons.

Normie, you...

You *can't* be serious.

HOO-
HAAAA!

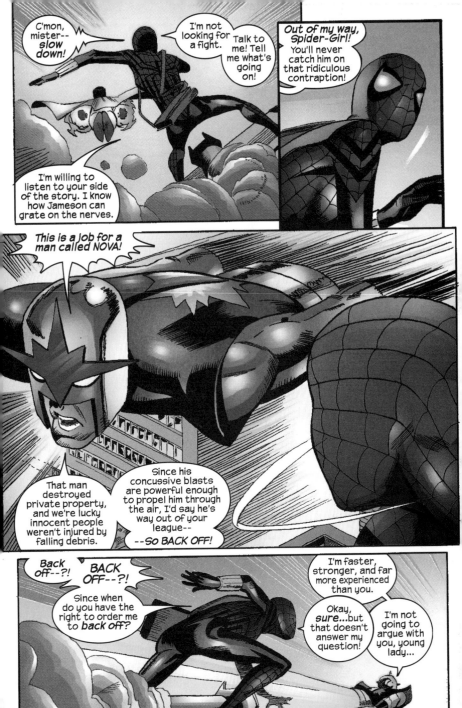

Way to go, girl!

It's about time you blasted Mr. Arrogance.

Unfortunately, you *did* allow the bad guy to escape--

--innocent people *were* threatened--

--you still *miss* your spider-powers--

--and your parents are going to have a *meltdown* when they hear that you've been playing *Spider-Goblin.*

Hoo-boy! At least things can't possibly get any worse--

--or *can* they?!

INDIG

CAF

INDIGO CAFE

Dinner Special

Filbert Stuffed Artichokes

Fried Tofu with Vegetables

THE END...for now!

APPROVED BY THE COMICS CODE AUTHORITY
SPIDER-GIRL
30
MARVEL COMICS
DEFALCO
OLLIFFE
WILLIAMSON

The daughter of the original Spider-Man, May "Mayday" Parker has inherited her father's amazing powers. Possessing the proportionate strength, speed and agility of a spider, as well as the ability to cling to walls, she now follows in his web-lines!

Stan Lee presents

SPIDER-GIRL!

Your name is *May "Mayday" Parker.*

Though you are the daughter of the original *Spider-Man,* you recently lost your spider-powers.

Since you're not ready to hang up your webs, you teamed up with a former enemy--

--and improvised a whole new *hero thing* for yourself.

And now, just to make life even more interesting, you've decided to test the *"new"* you--

Tom DeFalco & Pat Olliffe
script, plot & pencils
Al Williamson inker
Dave Sharpe letterer
Christie Scheele colorist
Frank Dunkerly asst. editor
Matt Hicks editor
Joe Quesada editor in chief

Mind if I ask a personal question, Spidey? Why are you so determined to stay in the hero game?

Why don't you just sit on the sidelines until your spider-powers return?

To be honest, Stinger... ...I'm not even sure they *will* come back.

And I can't quit until I tie up some loose ends.

Besides, I couldn't let all these nifty-keen *Goblin gizmos* go to waste.

As you can probably guess, I happen to believe there's a place in this world--

--for costumed heroes who aren't lucky enough to have *super powers.*

But I am curious how you came by that equipment.

The *Green Goblin* may be a criminal, but that's still his personal property.

I hope you didn't just *appropriate* it.

Even a noble end like yours doesn't justify *stealing!*

You tell *Normie Osborn* that you're heading home--

--and conveniently neglect to mention a quick side trip.

Yeah...*yeah*...I did hear that *Mr. Jameson* got into a thing with an unidentified costumed guy last night.

C'mon, Ms. Moore-- I'm sure a reporter like you knows all the details. Share the dirt!

I couldn't care less about the boss and his personal hijinks, Parker...

...but I did hear that he was arguing about some kind of secret project.

S'funny, how things turn out. You intended to focus on *Raptor* today.

You would have gladly left last night's mystery guy to *Nova* until *Tony Stark* opened his big, fat--*Whoa!* What's *he* doing here?

As I told your associate, Tony, I am taking every possible action to rectify the situation.

--and could that dye job be any more obvious?

Our licensing agreement is very specific. You should have notified me the instant *Project: Human Fly* went awry.

I know, Tony...but I can still fix everything.

Not good enough, Jonah.

I demand *results*, and I want them *yesterday*.

Is Stark always this pleasant--

Jonah, I have people who are specifically trained and equipped to deal with techno-thieves like the *Buzz*.

Way to go, girl!

The ball is now in Raptor's court.

All you have to do is sit back, and--

--*wait!?!*

Uhhh...

Hi, Dad.

Mom.

Uncle Phil.

We all spotted your message.

Couldn't miss it.

Did you forget to tell us something? When did your powers return?

T-they... didn't.

Then *why* are you still going out as *Spider-Girl?*

I have a responsibility to--

Don't even *try* to go there, young lady!

Your responsibilities as a super hero *ended* when you lost your spider-powers.

You're just an average teenager now.

Where did you scrounge up a *Goblin glider,* anyway?

N-Normie lent it to me.

N-Normie--? **NORMIE OSBORN?!?**

The same Normie who tried to kill you on at least three different occasions?

Normie isn't the problem, Peter. Your daughter should know better!

What are you trying to **PROVE?**

I... I'm not sure.

I just know that I was born to be *Spider-Girl* for a reason.

I am more than my powers--*a lot MORE*--and I just can't quit. *I can't!*

You have no choice, young lady.

You *Are* **GROUNDED!**

Grounded--?!?

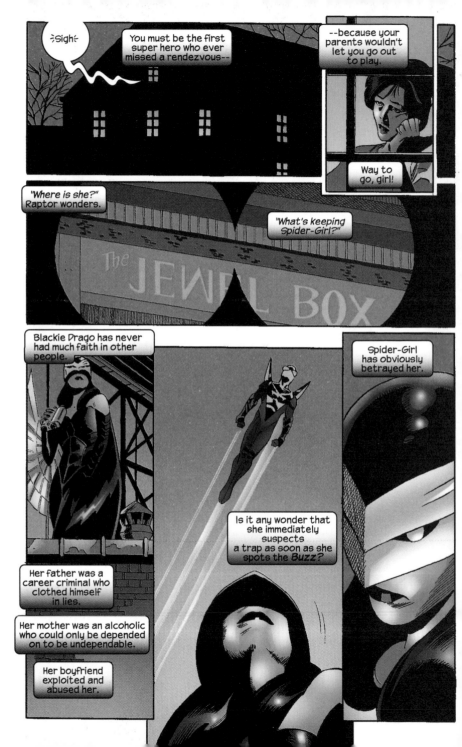

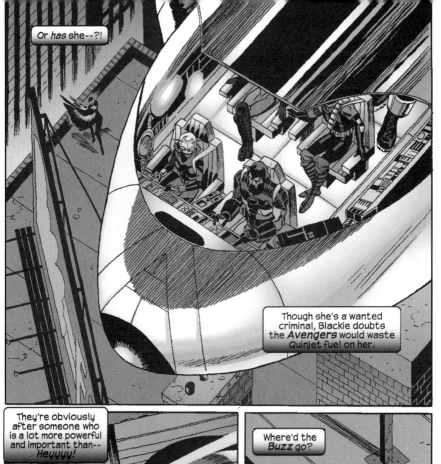

Or *has* she--?!

Though she's a wanted criminal, Blackie doubts the *Avengers* would waste Quinjet fuel on her.

They're obviously after someone who is a lot more powerful and important than-- *Heyyyy!*

The JEWEL

Where'd the *Buzz* go?

The rest of English class passes without incident, and then...

Kirby! Parker! I've been looking for you two. We gotta talk.

Something wrong, Coach Thompson?

Not at all! A golden opportunity just fell in our laps. I just got word that Nancy Lu may soon be joining us.

I don't know why she quit playing ball for Central, but we need her on our team.

Make friends with the girl, and convince her to join our program.

Do whatever's necessary! The whole team's depending on you.

I smell a **state championship!**

You can count on us, Coach.

Mayday and I will give Nancy *any*-thing--or any-one--she wants.

You're dancing awfully close to the line, Davida.

I really don't appreciate the way you keep--

Hey, guys! I hate to interrupt, but have you seen today's *Bugle?*

Looks like the *Avengers*--

--are assembling--

--against Spider-Girl's pal!

DAILY BUGLE

Saturday, February 19, 2012 Greater Metropolitan Edition

AVENGERS VOW, "WE'LL BUST THE BUZZ!"

Don't do anything *foolish?*

You are a super hero who has lost her powers--

--and now shares a secret headquarters with the man who used to be your greatest enemy.

Your best friend keeps needling because your *"boyfriend"* has been hanging around another girl--

--and you just blew him off to risk your neck for a guy you barely know.

Your parents are already furious with you--

--and will do a lot worse than ground you if they learn what you're planning.

Don't do anything *FOOLISH?!*

Isn't it more foolish to ditch an innocent man--

--than to defend him?

MARVEL COMICS
SPIDER-GIRL
#31
WWW.MARVEL.COM
DEFALCO
OLLIFFE
WILLIAMSON

The daughter of the original Spider-Man, May "Mayday" Parker has inherited her father's amazing powers. Possessing the proportionate strength, speed, and agility of a spider, as well as the ability to cling to walls, she now follows in his web-lines! *Stan Lee* presents...

SPIDER-GIRL!

"WITH FRIENDS LIKE *THESE*—"

Your name is *May "Mayday" Parker*, and you are the daughter of the original *Spider-Man.*

When you recently lost your *spider-powers*, you borrowed Normie Osborn's old *Green Goblin* equipment--

--and became a different kind of *Spider-Girl.*

However, beneath your new look, lurks the same old stubborn streak--

Tom DeFalco & Pat Olliffe
script, plot & pencils
Al Williamson inker
Dave Sharpe letterer
Christie Scheele colorist
Frank Dunkerly asst. editor
Matt Hicks editor
Joe Quesada editor in chief

--and that's why you've made a surprise visit to the New York offices of *Stark Global Enterprises.*

Freeze!

Please don't do anything rash!

A hostage negotiator is already on the way.

Please call her and extend my apologies for a false alarm.

I am *secure*, gentlemen, and today's password is *golden*.

The young lady's entrance may have been a tad unorthodox, but it was not totally unexpected.

I can give you three minutes, Spider-Girl. What do you want?

"I was minding my own business the other day... when this super-powered *mystery man* came bursting out of the *Daily Bugle*...and started a fight with me and *Nova*."

"According to my source, *you* initiated the altercation."

"Yeah...and I can guess your source... because the next thing I know, you suddenly appear...

...and order me to stay away from *Mister Mystery*.

"And then you grill me about a friend of mine called *the Buzz*.

"Later the same day...another friend spots you at the *Bugle* with someone...who just happens to match the description of my mystery man.

Well...

‹Uhhh›

I...I guess I should start at the beginning...

"The real kicker comes the following morning when the *Bugle* makes a special announcement.

"Coincidence? I think not."

DAILY BUGLE

Saturday, February 19, 2017 Greater Metropolitan Edition

AVENGERS VOW, "WE'LL BUST THE BUZZ!"

Why the sudden interest in *the Buzz*?

I'm going to indulge you, young lady... but only because you seem to have gained the respect of people I respect.

J. Jonah Jameson, the Bugle's publisher, recently funded a project to create a super hero.

Stark Global supplied him with certain proprietary technologies that he incorporated into a combat suit.

Someone stole the suit, and murdered the man chosen to operate it.

Since *the Buzz* currently has this suit, suspicion-- quite naturally-- falls on him.

For all the reasons you can imagine--and some you can't--I will not allow my work to remain in the hands of a murderer.

Look, I know how you must feel.

How *could* you?

Okay. Okay. I guess that was pretty lame, but I *do* know *the Buzz.*

We've worked together, and he's a good guy.

I can't--I *don't* believe he's a killer.

I'll take your opinion under advisement.

But I do wish you'd try to convince him to surrender.

He has absolutely *nothing* to fear from the authorities or me if he actually is *innocent.*

You have to admire the lady's restraint.

What do you mean?

I would have just gone through the window. She flew up the stairwell to the roof exit.

Based on your reading of the girl, what's her next move?

That's easy. She'll try to contact *the Buzz.*

You realize, of course, that I had to reimburse Jameson for his damage.

Every enterprise has expenses. You taught me that.

Follow her, and be prepared to execute a *P14.*

A-are you sure that's what you want, sir?

Now what?

Stark, the mystery guy, and the *Avengers* are all gunning for *the Buzz*--

--but he's a friend--

--and friends are supposed to stick up for each other.

That probably doesn't count if one of them is a *murderer...*

NO! He *can't* be guilty.

And...yet...his battle suit apparently belongs to *Jameson.*

Meanwhile, you still have no powers--

--and your parents will go ballistic if they ever learn that you're still doing your hero thing.

Mary Jane and I finally laid down the law.

We grounded May, and told her that her super hero days were over...

...until she regained her spider-powers.

Good for you! I'm glad you put your foot down. I was starting to worry about her myself.

POLICE
MIDTOWN SOUTH

RIING

Peter Parker, please. I'm an old friend.

Pete--?

Johnny Storm.

Look, guy, I hate to bother you at work...but I'm here at *Fantastic Five* headquarters...and we just got the strangest call from *Tony Stark*.

S-she *what--?!?*

Some-thing wrong, Pete?

Pete--?!

Your father doesn't want you hanging with me?

He's still carrying a lot of old baggage, Normie...and doesn't realize how much you've changed.

I'm not all that surprised. I did try to kill him a few months ago.

You, too, for that matter.

Why dwell on past mistakes when we can make new ones?

Speaking of your current stupidity, this gizmo may come in handy if the *Avengers* take exception to your friendship with *the Buzz.*

It releases an electro-magnetic pulse that may throw *Mainframe* off-line for a few minutes.

I hope to avoid a fight. Violence never solves anything--

--and I'm buds with *Stinger* and *American Dream.*

Look, I'm glad you don't desert people...

I'd still be the *Green Goblin,* if not for you.

But I wish you'd reconsider.

If you must save someone, you should concentrate on *Raptor.*

At least she claims she wants to *retire* from crime--

--and the Avengers aren't after *her.*

I promise to give Raptor my full attention--

--*after* I've gotten Stark off the Buzz's back.

I know you mean well, Normie--

--but an innocent man shouldn't have to suffer--

--because I failed to act.

Everybody, CHILL! Nobody wants to look like a *jerk* by starting a big fight over some silly *misunderstanding!*

I suggest we retire to the nearest rooftop, and try to sort things out like adults.

Sounds good to me!

Big whoop! You're not the one they're trying to nail. Why should I trust these guys?

You don't have much choice. We have you surrounded.

This isn't the time to go *macho* on me, Mainframe! I need you to play *nice.*

Spider-Girl is practically one of us. She wouldn't stand up for the Buzz if she thought he was a murderer.

I believe we owe her the courtesy of listening to her reasons for--

≥ARRRGH≤

Stinger--!

Y-you were playing *possum!*

A calculated gamble.

I had to get close enough to remove Mr. Stark's technology.

What about the *Buzz?* If you've harmed him--!

T-throttle down, girl! I...I seem to be... *what?*

Oh!

According to my internal diagnostic... some of my sub-systems are off-line...but I...I'm still functional.

Too bad he couldn't delete your *'tude.*

Is *that* what this was all about? Tony Stark mobilized the *Avengers,* sacrificed *Stinger,* and put all our *lives* in danger--

--*just because he wanted his TOYS back?*

I suppose you could see it like that.

By the way, I've been in touch with the *Avengers...* and *Stinger* is fine.

Please believe me when I tell you that her health was never at risk.

Why should we suddenly trust *you?*

I don't *lie,* Spider-Girl.

You could have *avoided* this entire situation if you had only *listened* to Mr. Stark--

--and convinced the *Buzz* to surrender.

MARVEL COMICS
THE STEEL SPIDER STRIKES!
SPIDER-GIRL
#32
WWW.MARVEL.COM
APPROVED BY THE COMICS CODE AUTHORITY
DEFALCO
OLLIFFE
WILLIAMSON

The daughter of the original Spider-Man, May "Mayday" Parker has inherited her father's amazing powers. Possessing the proportionate strength, speed and agility of a spider, as well as the ability to cling to walls, she now follows in his web-lines! *Stan Lee presents...*

SPIDER-GIRL!

Whazzat--?!

It's just the wind, Frank.

Try to relax, huh?

I can't concentrate with you yammering in my ear.

I can't help it, Matt. I keep hearing...

Uh-oh!

Stop this crime! Desist at once, or face the terrible wrath of--

--THE **STEEL SPIDER!**

Tom DeFalco & Pat Olliffe script, plot & pencils
Al Williamson inker
Dave Sharpe letterer
Christie Scheele colorist
Frank Dunkerly asst. editor
Matt Hicks editor
Joe Quesada editor in chief

Snap out of it, girl! With or without your spider-powers, you need to get your head **back** into the hero game, and--

Whoa! Someone seems to be in a hurry!

Oh!

Yeah. S-sorry, May...I...I'm a little distracted.

Is something **wrong**, Courtney? You look kinda **flushed**.

H-how do you expect me to **look** after-- ohmygosh!

Y-you haven't heard, **have you?** You don't know about the **accident.**

Accident--?!

I-it happened at football practice yesterday. **Moose** was trying to tackle somebody. H-he must have landed **wrong**...or something...

...because he...he **broke** his leg.

The whole gang went to the hospital last night.

Except for **you.**

I--I didn't **know.**

How could you? I tried to call you a few times, but your parents kept answering the phone.

They seemed pretty revved about something...so I didn't leave a message.

Every-thing **cool** on the home front?

No... not really, Davida...is...is Moose going to be **okay?**

The leg will eventually heal...but his football days could be **over.**

Davida's right! You've been so caught up with all the super hero silliness that you've been neglecting your friends.

Take *Jack Jameson*, for example-- you blew him off the other day because the *Buzz* needed your help.

Maybe it's time you made amends...

Hey, JJ! Headed for the cafeteria?

Well, well, if it isn't the ever-elusive *Ms. Parker!* What can I do for you, pretty lady?

I was wondering if we could share a soda o' something.

Time out! I can't believe you actually have an opening in your busy social schedule.

Okay, I deserve that. I have been a little distant lately.

Lady, you been *MIA!*

I can relate.

I've had my own share of problems recently, and I needed a friend...

So I found *one!*

You ready for lunch, Nancy?

Just as long as they aren't serving manicotti again.

Ha! You out-smarted yourself, woman. We have you completely surrounded, and ⸮UGGNN⸮

I hate to interrupt you in mid-gloat, but I'm glad you closed ranks.

It's a lot easier to clobber you when you're all bunched together.

You GO, girl! You flattened *six* of them in as many seconds.

I've got to kick into high gear just to keep pace.

KPA

KWOOM!

You truly believe that the Soldiers of the Serpent would come unprepared for the likes of you?

Get ready to leap on my signal--!

To where-- *Kansas* ?!?

A *gentleman* never threatens a lady...but I guess *you* wouldn't know about that!

Who *dares*--?!

That would be me.

Smile, my friend! You're about to make history.

I've just decided to start the rest of my life, and you are going to be my leadoff super-conquest.

Cool, *huh*?

With a little luck, your picture will appear on posters and trading cards.

You ready to rumble?

Your bravado obviously exceeds your wisdom.

My *laser cannon* will incinerate you where you stand!

Like the Rock says, JUST BRING IT!

Oops! Looks like somebody needs to adjust his targeting array.

Get OUT of my way, sweet thing!

S-sweet thing--?! D-did you just call me sweet thing?!

Sorry if I offended you, hon-- --but your *feelings* take a back seat to this woman's *safety!*

No *innocent* will ever suffer because *Spider-Man* failed to act!

I...I can't thank you enough, young man.

It was my pleasure, ma'am. I was taught to believe that with *great power* there should also come *great responsibility.*

Say *whaaaaa--?!*

That costumed CREEP has gone too FAR!

Not only has he stolen my *name* and *costume*, he even seems to have found a way to mimic my *powers.*

If I didn't know better, I'd swear *Mysterio* has risen from the grave again.

This is just the kind of stunt he used to pull in the old days.

Yeah, but that's when you guys still had a *thing* going.

Neither one of you has been active for--*what?* *Fifteen? Sixteen* years now?!

You don't understand, Phil. This is *personal!* Someone is trying to steal my identity.

He may plan to ruin my reputation or draw me out of retirement.

Can't understand--?!

Phil Urich's own career as a super hero was cut unmercifully short.

He was recently replaced as Spider-Girl's mentor by one of her former enemies.

CAN'T understand--?!

As much as he'd like to voice his own complaints, Phil knows this *isn't* about him.

And so he extends a steady arm--

--and whispers words of comfort and support.

You CAN'T understand!

He's trying to *replace* me!

Maybe the new Spidey is right!

Who needs a powerless *Spider-Girl* when you can have a fully-functional *Spider-Man?*

Why are you *clinging* to the hero biz--

--when even your own parents think you should *quit?!*

Isn't this *comfy?*

Davida, JJ and *Nancy*-- looks like everyone's having a *fine time!*

Everyone--

--except--

--you.

Yo, Mayday-- *you okay?*

You look a little down.

Hey, *Brad...*

Why the long face?

Any-thing I can do?

*Nah...*every-thing's fine... *really!* Believe it or not, I was just thinking about science class--

--and how everything is constantly *evolving* around us.

Nancy Lu used to go to Central High.

She was the star of their basketball team until you learned that she was a *mutant*--

--who was secretly using her powers to enhance her play.

Unlike a certain someone who once had the proportionate *strength, speed* and *agility* of a spider.

S'funny, you suddenly realize how much you've *missed* competing with her...

Blast that Normie Osborn!

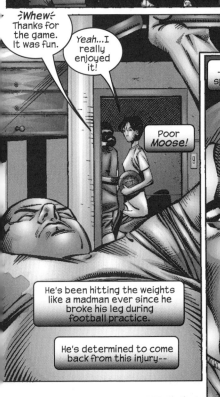

⸗Whew⸗ Thanks for the game. It was fun.

Yeah...I really enjoyed it!

Poor *Moose!*

He's been hitting the weights like a madman ever since he broke his leg during football practice.

He's determined to come back from this injury--

--and *regain* his spot on the team.

No one's going to replace *him!*

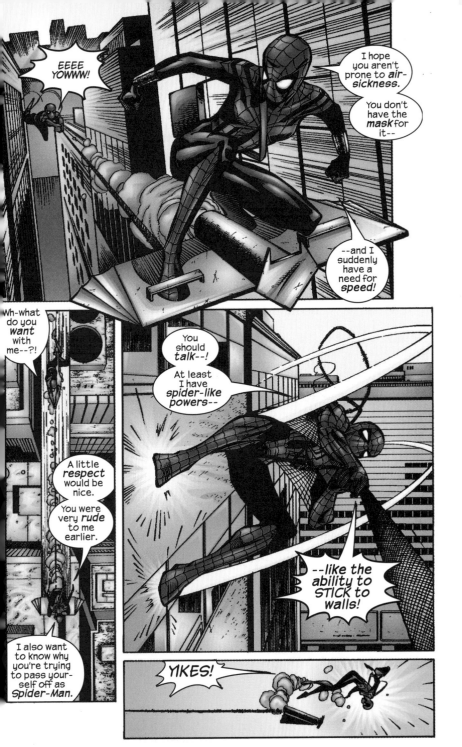

SPIDER-MAN DEAD?

You home already?

How was today's patrol?

To be honest, Mom...it was a little embarrassing!

I ran into *Spider-Girl* again, and she made me look like a big jerk.

I'm sorry to hear that, son.

She says she knows the real *Spider-Man*, and questions my *right* to the name.

Does she--?

That's *interesting*----and it pretty well *confirms* my suspicions about her.

Maybe we shouldn't have copied the costume, but you certainly have a legitimate claim to the name.

Trust me, son! You were always destined to be the next *Spider-Man*.

THE END... for now!